1. Landscape of west Cornwall

The popularity of west Cornwall stems from the varied and ~~~~ ~~~~ that encourages an endless flow of visitors across the Tamar. Many of you come perhaps to laze on the golden sands of its beaches, some of you will explore the cliffs and moorland whilst others are drawn to villages that once served fisherfolk, or miners and their families.

Penberth Cove, a fishing hamlet between Land's End and Penzance.

Since 1965, the Enterprise Neptune Appeal has allowed the National Trust to acquire, manage and conserve many important stretches of coastline in Cornwall. The coastal footpaths were partly established by members of the coastguard service in the course of their work. They have been extended and maintained with minimum effect on the natural state of the landscape. They now serve splendidly as a means of access to some of the finest seascapes imaginable, constantly changing at the whim of weather and tide.

This account of contrasting landscapes and underlying rock formations will give visitors an insight into what lies beneath their favourite leisure spots, be they beaches, cliffs, moors or quaint historic villages. It is fully illustrated and gently ushers the reader through explanations of geological processes in readily understandable terms. The mining industry is also described at a time when its ruins have at last been recognised as a valuable part of our national heritage.

Three contrasting landscapes can be readily recognized in this part of Cornwall, resulting from distinctly different underlying rock formations. The most southerly part of the area, and indeed the most southerly part of mainland Britain, is the **Lizard Peninsula,** largely cut off by the Helford River. The rocks from which much of the Lizard is carved are of great variety and essentially different from the rest of Cornwall. Many millions of years ago during a period of great movement within the earth's crust, the rocks that make up the Lizard were pushed up from the ocean floor onto the margin of the land along a major fault. Some of these rocks are very hard, and some, like the famous serpentine which is carved into ornaments, rather soft. The profile of the Lizard when viewed from Mount's Bay or Falmouth Bay forms a knife-edge skyline, broken only by the satellite communication dishes on Goonhilly Downs and the turbines of the nearby wind farm. The gentle flat inland moors meet the sea along modest cliffs for much of the jagged coastline.

Wind turbines at Bonython.

Away from the Lizard, and separated from it by a fault, softer rocks form much of the **low rolling country**. Dark mud with thin silt layers was compressed into slate of which much of the south coast is formed whereas the north coast consists of slate and sandstone layers. The sea has eroded these softer rocks more easily, working in a pincer movement to form St Ives and Mount's bays.

The moorlands of the **Land's End Peninsula,** the high ground around **Carnmenellis**, between Camborne and Falmouth, and the smaller areas of Tregonning and Godolphin hills and St Michael's Mount are all formed of granite. This is an igneous rock which began its molten life deep within the earth's crust. The massive granite cliffs of Land's End are Cornwall's first line of defence against the sheer force of the Atlantic storms. If, by some quirk of nature, the Land's End Granite did not exist, the south-west peninsula of England would probably terminate in granite cliffs somewhere between Camborne and Helston. The rounded landscape is locally broken by tors. These upstanding irregular masses of granite rock are natural monuments to the processes of erosion which have taken place around them.

Sunset over St Michael's Mount.

Some of the most distinctive and well-loved features associated with the Cornish landscape are the remains of its **mining industry**. Tin and copper mining have ceased with the exception of a single mine near Camborne, the future of which can only be described as tenuous. The mines worked narrow veins of ore which penetrate both granite and slate and occur in a broad belt crossing the area from St Just to Redruth and beyond. Local memories of the miners, some just boys, toiling in dark, dank and dangerous caverns are fast fading. The derelict and crumbling buildings are assuming the romantic image usually reserved for cathedrals or castles.

Robinson's Shaft at South Crofty Mine.

Changes in sea level over the last 20 million years have given rise to flat erosional features of the landscape including the old marine platform forming the surface of the Lizard. A similar but slightly higher platform surrounds the Land's End Peninsula. The seas of earlier times had little respect for the various rock types, planing them down to a uniform level. Raised beaches, submerged forests and drowned valleys are further proof that sea level fell but rose again over the last twenty thousand years.

Whilst exploring this area, you will begin to appreciate that west Cornwall's landscape is a delicate balance between the forces of Nature and the labours of Mankind. Some parts are unsullied whereas others have been devastated as a result of mineral exploitation. Man's prehistoric monuments, his desecration of the countryside by mining, even his division of the land by a mosaic of stone hedges, and more recently the excesses of the holiday industry are all superimposed upon Nature's own form. It is to be hoped that the recent spread of Man's artifacts, do not significantly upset this balance.

A Celtic granite cross near St Buryan.

Wind turbines at Bonython and satellite communications dishes at Goonhilly Downs.

2. Lizard Peninsula

Cornish heath

Erica vagans

The Lizard Peninsula is a designated Area of Outstanding Natural Beauty and, apart from a few incursions of the twentieth century such as the Goonhilly Earth Station, the nearby wind farm at Bonython and Predannack Airfield, it retains a very peculiar charm. Curiosity about the name itself is the visitor's first reaction. It is familiar in modern English but there are records from the eleventh century, with a variety of spellings, which indicate a derivation from the Cornish 'Lys ardh' meaning 'court on a height'. The court is thought to have occupied an area of the headland where Lizard Town now stands and to have been the court of a prince or possibly a group of Irish monks. Sabine Baring-Gould in his guide to Cornwall suggested that the peninsula should properly be called Meneage, 'the land of the Minachau, the monks'.

'Unique' is the epithet most commonly and justifiably applied to the landscape of the Lizard. A major reason for this feeling of difference is the underlying fabric of the peninsula, its geology. Real mementoes of this district, which distinguish it from many others with their universal souvenirs, are the colourful polished serpentine ornaments fashioned from the local bedrock. A favourite with the early turners, and still obtainable, are the miniature lighthouses. Lizard serpentine is part of a rock association found nowhere else in Britain and the connection with the sea is most apt. After forming in the earth's crust beneath a deep ocean some 380 million years ago, this piece of ocean crust was pushed up by a collision between continents.

Typical serpentine ornaments.

90-metre erosion surface of the Lizard viewed from the west at Porthleven.

A typical section of the earth's crust beneath the deep oceans is about six kilometres thick. Beneath the crust is the Upper Mantle, a layer about 200 kilometres thick, consisting of melted and solid rocks called **peridotites** which are made of magnesium and iron silicates. Ocean crust forms when the thicker and lighter continental crust splits apart and molten rock, or magma, from the mantle fills the gap and solidifies. These crustal rocks are largely coarsely crystalline **gabbros**. During a long consolidation process some magma escapes up fractures through previously consolidated gabbro where it cools quickly forming finely crystalline **basalt dykes** (veins). Magma that escapes to the top of the crust forms **lavas** on the ocean floor.

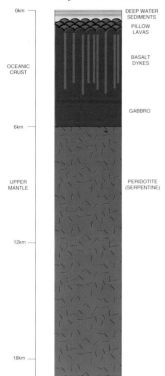

Section of the ocean crust.

0km	DEEP WATER SEDIMENTS
	PILLOW LAVAS
OCEANIC CRUST	BASALT DYKES
	GABBRO
6km	
UPPER MANTLE	PERIDOTITE (SERPENTINE)
12km	
18km	

Basalt dyke cutting gabbro on the foreshore near Coverack.

The change from the rolling countryside, wooded valleys and inlets, to the flat, barren downland that dominates the landscape as you travel southwards into the peninsula reflects the change from slate and sandstone country to the crystalline rocks of the Lizard. The road is bordered by hedges which lean away from the prevailing south westerly winds and the landscape is largely treeless, except in valleys which afford some protection. This plateau is cut locally by small streams but generally slopes very gently from the centre of the peninsula to the coasts from around 100 metres to about 75 metres above present sea level and is termed the 90-metre platform. It was formed fairly recently geologically speaking, about four million years ago when the sea was at a higher level than now. The shallow sea covered the rocks of the Lizard area and the coastline was located around the Carnmenellis Granite. Wave action and sea currents planed off the sea bed to a smooth surface at more or less the level of the present land surface. On **Crousa Downs** there are small excavations into pebble gravels

A hedge leaning away from prevailing sou'westerlies.

Residual blocks of gabbro known locally as 'crusairs' on parts of Crousa Downs.

Curlew

Numenius arquata

made of quartz, quite unlike the solid rocks beneath. Until recently these gravels were thought to have been banks of pebbles that washed around that sea bed and remained stranded when that sea retreated. The latest work suggests that they are river gravels of more recent origin. Where the gabbro is not covered by gravel and associated clay, there are numerous boulders locally known as 'crusairs', scattered about the fields and downs or gathered up into the field boundaries. These are now thought to have come out of the clay and gravel deposits where these have been worn away.

Just down the road from Crousa Common is the very pleasant old fishing village of **Coverack** where you can walk upon the northern foreshore made of gabbro which formed deep in that ocean crust 380 million years ago. Those with keen eyes may also see the finer, dark, basaltic dykes, less than a metre wide, that strike across the shore in a north westerly direction. The rocks at the southern end of the beach are different to the trained eye as they are not from the ancient crust but from deep in the mantle. They are peridotites that are locally altered by hydration to serpentine, a name derived from its resemblance to the patterns of snakeskin. However, much more typical as the serpentine used for souvenirs is the rock at Kynance Cove.

The harbour at Coverack.

Kynance Cove was a popular visiting place in Victorian times because of its superb sands, clear waters and a fascination with the serpentine industry, then at its height. It is still a fine place to visit for the cliff scenery and the rocks. Partially serpentinized peridotite, a dark greenish-black rock locally with red and brown staining, is present by the paths to the cove. In the cliffs behind the centre and western part of the cove most of the peridotite is made over to serpentine which is coloured variously green, red and brown with a strong streaky appearance.

Cliffs carved out of multi-coloured serpentine rock at Kynance Cove.

There are numerous cross-cutting dykes of dark basalt and veins of pale granite, and next to some of the granite veins in the western part of the cove the serpentine is altered to soft talc. Talcose 'soap rock' or steatite was quarried between the 1740's and 1850 just along the cliffs from Kynance at Gew-graze, sometimes known as Soapy Cove. Discovered by Cornishman, William Borlase, the first recorded use of Cornish steatite in soft-paste porcelain was in 1748 at Bristol by Benjamin Lund and William Miller. This venture was short-lived before being taken over in 1752 by the Worcester Porcelain Company, founded in the previous year. The Wedgwood brothers, Dr Thomas and Josiah, first examined Gew-graze in 1849 but were unimpressed with the quality of the deposit. Josiah returned to Cornwall in

Bloody cranesbill

Geranium sanguineum

Serpentine turning by Derek Pitman of 'Quality Serpentine'.

1775 to examine various sources of clay but showed no interest in Gew-graze which was then managed by the discoverer of Cornish china clay, William Cookworthy, 'working' in retirement for the Worcester Porcelain Company. Although china clay was discovered locally in 1746 it was not used to make hard-paste porcelain until 1768. Steatite production figures are not well known but a maximum annual total of twelve tons has been recorded.

The idea of polishing serpentine may have originated when farmers placed large upright blocks of the stone in fields for the cattle to rub against. The largely cottage-based industry of serpentine turning was established nearly two hundred years ago in sheds and lean-tos near Lizard Town. A factory built in the last century at Poltesco has all but vanished. Today there are just a handful of family businesses making traditional knick-knacks for which the locality is famous. Queen Victoria visited the Lizard in 1846 and like many tourists since, took home some examples of local craftsmanship in this wonderfully appealing stone. The raw material has been obtained from small pits on Lizard Downs between Lizard Town and Kynance Cove, each turner having a favourite and usually secret source. Serpentine was also used as a building stone. Examples of this can be seen in St Winwalloes Church at Landewednack, east of Lizard Town where it is used in conjunction with granite from Carnmenellis, and at the Three Tuns Inn at St Keverne.

Jackdaw at Cadgwith

Corvus monedula

Blocks of darker serpentine and paler granite used in the construction of the tower of Landewednack Church.

Most people will visit **Lizard Point,** the southernmost spot on mainland Britain and if you have already seen the massive gabbro and serpentine rocks it will be quite apparent that the rocks hereabouts are different. They were once mudstone, sandstone and lava, similar to those around Falmouth and Penzance. When the ancient ocean closed and the Lizard rocks were torn from the ocean floor, the rocks onto which they were pushed were subjected to great pressure and high temperatures. Under those conditions they changed mineralogically and new platy minerals crystalized in alignment, giving the rocks a strongly layered appearance. These are the rocks of Lizard Point and they are known to the geologist as *schist*. This is a term which is used to describe a type of rock which has undergone a change of its constituent minerals, part of a group of rocks described by geologists as *metamorphic*, meaning literally, change of shape.

Hottentot fig

Carpobrotus edulis

On the coast on the western side of the road and track from Lizard Town, the rock is full of platy micas which produce shiny surfaces that glint in the sunlight; these were sandstone and mudstone. To the east are different dark-green laminated rocks with a fine silky texture; these were once lava.

Cadgwith Cove.

A collapsed cave: the Devil's Frying Pan near Cadgwith.

Just south of the picture postcard village of **Cadgwith** is the collapsed cave of Hugga Driggee, better known to countless visitors as the Devil's Frying-pan. The 'pan' is a funnel-shaped cavity in the cliff connected to the sea by the 'handle', a water-filled gully beneath a natural rock-arch. A fault which separates schist on the south from serpentine with granite intrusions to the north was the focal point of the erosional power of the sea.

Mullion Cove and Island.

Mullion Cove is situated at the mouth of a small, steep valley which drains the north western part of the Lizard plateau. The rocks to the south of the valley are mainly serpentine and those to the north mainly schist. It is a typically attractive Cornish fishing haven from which smuggling was inevitably conducted. Just offshore, Mullion Island is home to numerous seabirds including a breeding colony of Lesser

Lesser Black-backed Gull

Black-backed Gulls. The island consists of pillows of basaltic lava that formed on the ancient sea floor from below which the rocks of the Lizard were derived.

Larus fuscus

As you retreat from the coasts across the downs, and particularly if you tarry to enjoy the variety of the Lizard heathland plants, the flat open spaces dotted with ancient burial mounds give an atmosphere of timeless isolation and quiet. Perhaps you can appreciate now that it was not always so.

East side of the Lizard looking towards Black Head from Landewed-nack showing the flat 90-metre erosional surface.

3. Low rolling country

Lying to the north of the Lizard is gently rolling country with treeless, flat-topped hills cut by steep-sided, wooded valleys. Between the higher granite moorland of the Land's End Peninsula and Carnmenellis is a broad swathe of heavily farmed land. The natural characteristics of the area are due to the softer underlying slate and sandstone, and different proportions of these rock types have given rise to varied coastal scenery. The wide sandy bays and low cliffs of Mount's Bay and St Ives' Bay are formed in the dark slate which underlies most of the area. In contrast, the high cliffs of the northern coast and those east of Porthleven are formed

Crithmum maritimum

from harder sandstone interlayered with the slate, making the rocks considerably more resistant to erosion by the sea. Although beds of sandstone and slate also form the southern coast around the Helford River and Carrick Roads, the cliffs here are not so high, partly because the more sheltered south coast has not been eroded by the full force of Atlantic storms. The more powerful southerly draining streams have cut a complex pattern of valleys and inlets which characterize the southern Cornish coast, giving it unparalleled scenic charm.

Cliffs of sandstone and slate on the north coast near Porthtowan.

Along the coast between Carrick Roads and the Helford River and in the cliffs west of Loe Bar near Porthleven, you will observe the repeated layers or beds of slate and sandstone known as *turbidites*. They were formed in a now vanished ocean which stretched southwards from southern Cornwall 370 million years ago. The beds of dark grey slate which underlie much of the central and western part of this area are also turbidites, but they were deposited further out at sea. The layers in the slate are thinner since less of the sand and mud from rivers draining into this ocean was able to reach this far from shore.

The sheltered waters of the Helford River.

Beds of graded sandy turbidites.

Thin muddy and silty turbidite beds near Porthleven.

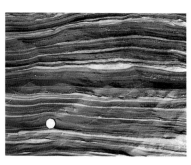

Turbidites

Rivers discharge their load of mud and sand into the sea, especially during times of flood, where it sinks towards the sea bed. There it forms a liquid slurry, which is denser than sea water. This flows downslope scouring channels into the sea bed and is known as a turbidity current. When the current begins to slow, the sand and mud settle out on the level floor of the ocean. The heavier, coarser sand settles first followed by progressively finer sand and silt and finally by mud.

The alternating layers of sandstone and mudstone deposited by this process are characteristically graded, with coarser sand at the base of each layer fining upwards to mud at the top. Turbidites can form thick piles of predominantly sandy layers each up to a few metres thick. The finer silt and mud, carried further out to sea by the current form thin alternating layers of pale silt and dark mud – the typical slate of west Cornwall.

Oyster catcher

Haematopus ostralegus

An alternating mudstone and sandstone turbidite sequence on the foreshore of the Helford River.

Between Falmouth and Loe Bar near Porthleven, thick layers of jumbled rock fragments, varying from a few centimetres to the size of a house, are enclosed in dark grey slate. These rocks formed as the result of *submarine landslides* which took place during the deposition of the turbidites in the unstable environment of a *subduction zone*. Around Falmouth they contain small rock fragments of different colours giving them a rather blobby appearance but much larger rock fragments can be seen in the cliffs between Loe Bar and Porthleven.

Submarine Landslides

Submarine landslides occur where mud and sand are rapidly deposited from rivers flowing into the sea to form a thick pile on the sloping sea floor. When the pile becomes too thick, or is shaken by an earthquake, part of it can collapse and slide downwards towards the deep ocean floor. The deposits formed by submarine landslides are commonly made up of a variety of different types of rock, varying from small pebbles up to blocks several kilometres in size, set in a clay mass. Because sand and mud accumulate rapidly in the sea adjacent to **subduction zones,** *where earthquakes are particularly frequent, submarine landslips are characteristic of a subduction zone environment. Their presence in old rocks such as those around Falmouth and Porthleven suggest that a subduction zone existed in this area about 380 to 360 million years ago.*

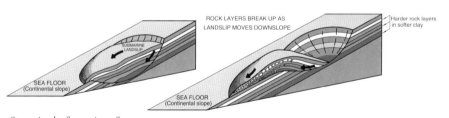

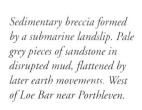

Stages in the formation of a submarine landslip.

Sedimentary breccia formed by a submarine landslip. Pale grey pieces of sandstone in disrupted mud, flattened by later earth movements. West of Loe Bar near Porthleven.

Subduction and collision

The earth's crust is a solid skin between six and 30 kilometres thick which floats on a layer of heavier, semi-molten rocks within the upper 100 kilometres of the earth's interior. The crust itself is broken into a number of large plates which are moved around very slowly by currents in the Earth's interior. **When plates move apart**, lava from the underlying semi-molten rocks is squeezed into the gap between them and

solidifies to form new crust. This six kilometre thick veneer of oceanic crust underlies the oceans and contrasts with the thicker, older, continental crust. The formation of new ocean floor is presently taking place in the middle of the Atlantic Ocean in a zone extending from the Arctic to the Antarctic and is causing the characteristically "gentle" volcanic activity seen in Iceland.

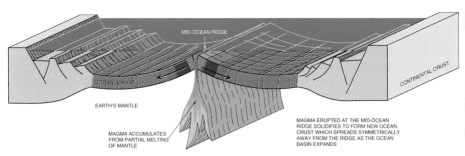

MID-OCEAN RIDGE

OCEAN CRUST

CONTINENTAL CRUST

EARTH'S MANTLE

MAGMA ACCUMULATES FROM PARTIAL MELTING OF MANTLE

MAGMA ERUPTED AT THE MID-OCEAN RIDGE SOLIDIFIES TO FORM NEW OCEAN CRUST WHICH SPREADS SYMMETRICALLY AWAY FROM THE RIDGE AS THE OCEAN BASIN EXPANDS

In other places, **plates are sliding past each other**. The immense frictional forces involved along the geological faults between the plates causes them to slide past each other with a jerky motion, each jerk

generating an earthquake. The earthquakes affecting Los Angeles and San Francisco are caused by this process as two crustal plates slide past each other along the San Andreas Fault.

San Andreas Fault crossing the Carrizo Plain: sliding plates.

Fissure eruption, Krafla, Iceland: the formation of new crust as plates move apart.

When plates move towards each other, the relatively thin ocean crust is pushed down into the earth's interior, melted and overridden by the other plate. This type of structure is known

as a **subduction zone**. Volcanoes which result from the melting are characterized by the violence of their eruptions, Mount St. Helens and Mount Mayon are examples.

The 1968 eruption of Mayon Volcano, Phillippines: a violent eruption caused by subduction and melting.

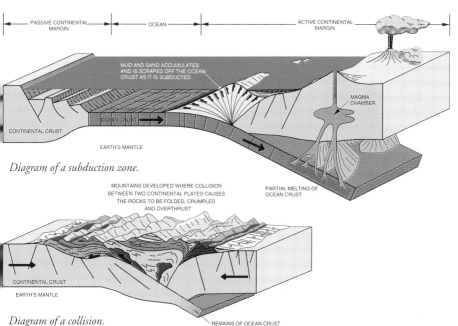

PASSIVE CONTINENTAL MARGIN — OCEAN — ACTIVE CONTINENTAL MARGIN

MUD AND SAND ACCUMULATES AND IS SCRAPED OFF THE OCEAN CRUST AS IT IS SUBDUCTED

MAGMA CHAMBER

CONTINENTAL CRUST

OCEAN CRUST

EARTH'S MANTLE

Diagram of a subduction zone.

PARTIAL MELTING OF OCEAN CRUST

MOUNTAINS DEVELOPED WHERE COLLISION BETWEEN TWO CONTINENTAL PLATES CAUSES THE ROCKS TO BE FOLDED, CRUMPLED AND OVERTHRUST

CONTINENTAL CRUST

EARTH'S MANTLE

Diagram of a collision.

REMAINS OF OCEAN CRUST

Continued movement of the plates towards each other eventually brings together the continents on either side of the ocean. Because the crust which forms the continents is much thicker (30 kilometres) and lighter than oceanic crust it cannot be pushed into the earth's interior. Instead the continents on either side of the vanished ocean collide with each other. The force of such a **collision** is so great that the rocks themselves are crumpled and pushed upwards to form a mountain chain along the line of the collision. Over the immense span of geological time, wind and rain erode away the upper part of the mountain chain, leaving only a low lying area of crumpled rocks as evidence of its existence. The crumpled and folded rocks that we now see in Cornwall, are part of the eroded remnants of such a mountain chain which 300 million years ago may have been as massive as the Himalayas are today. The rocks of the Lizard are a fragment of the crust of the vanished ocean caught up in the collision.

Volcanic rock squeezed as a liquid magma between layers of slate, Porthleven.

Volcanic activity, taking place on the floor of the ocean in which the dark slate was being deposited some 370 million years ago, gave rise to several different types of rocks which are now visible along the foreshore and in the cliffs of Mount's Bay and around St Ives. The volcanic rocks are mostly dark green and very hard. They were squeezed upwards in the form of molten lava along steep fractures and into layers a few metres thick in the slate where the lava cooled and solidified. Some of these rocks can be seen on the foreshore at **Porthleven**. In some places these sheets were accompanied by large volumes of lava. These are very resistant to sea erosion and form prominent cliffs in Mount's Bay between St Michael's Mount and Cudden Point. At **Penlee Quarry**, just south of Newlyn, a similar mass of volcanic rock has been extensively quarried but the site is not currently in use. The exceptional hardness of this rock has made it valuable as an aggregate in concrete for the construction of bank vaults.

Herring Gull

Larus argentatus

Volcanic rocks were also erupted onto the surface. Masses of fragmented lava produced by the repeated eruption and congealing of lava in a vent, form a rock composed of a mosaic of different coloured angular pieces. Rocks of this type indicate the site of an underwater volcano in the reefs known as **Great Hogus** between Marazion and Penzance. Where these volcanoes discharged lava onto the ancient sea floor, the interaction between the hot lava and cold seawater formed the distinctive *pillow lava* which can be seen in superb exposures at **Burthallan Cliff**, west of St Ives.

Fragmented lava from a volcanic vent, Great Hogus, Marazion.

16

Pillow lava

A profusion of lava pillows with inset showing details at Burthallan Cliff, St Ives.

We normally have an image of volcanoes as large conical mountains on land. However, most of the world's volcanoes actually occur under the sea. Although lava erupting from a volcano on land is cooled relatively slowly by the air and therefore generally forms large sheetlike flows beneath a thin solidifying skin, often wrinkled by the motion of the liquid lava beneath, lava erupting from volcanoes on the sea floor behaves very differently. When it erupts from an underwater vent it is immediately chilled by contact with the water, forming a relatively thin plastic skin over a molten interior. As lava continues to flow out of the vent it inflates the plastic skin like a balloon. Unlike a balloon, however, the skin can only stretch a small amount before it splits allowing the molten lava in its interior to spill out. This molten lava forms a new skin on contact with the water which is in turn inflated by the continuing flow of lava. This process happens over and over again. The lava flow from an underwater vent therefore consists of a large number of these rounded lava masses, up to a metre in diameter, that look rather like a pile of pillows - hence the name "pillow lava". Pillow lavas are therefore a characteristic product of underwater volcanoes.

Alignment of minerals forming cleavage in slate seen under the microscope and magnified (×1500).

All of the rocks in this part of Cornwall were folded and faulted during a period of continental collision 360 million years ago which crumpled and pushed them up from below sea level to form the Cornish landmass. During this process the initially weak beds of sandstone and mudstone were compressed and hardened. In the mudstone this compression caused the formation of tiny platy minerals called mica to become aligned like the pages in a book. Because they could be easily split or cleaved into thin sheets for roofing slates, the mineral alignment is known as *cleavage* and the rock itself is called *slate*.

Folds and thrusts

Most of us think of rocks as being hard and brittle. However, the enormous pressure and increased temperature at depth within the earth's crust allows even the hardest of rocks to behave like soft plastic. When subjected to the titanic forces which prevail during continental collision, rocks will bend, fold and sometimes flow. The rock layers visible along the Cornish coast were originally horizontal and have been compressed into regular folds during continental collision about 360 million years ago.

In some places compression has caused the rock to break along shallow-dipping fractures known as thrusts. Thrusts are a type of geological fault in which the rocks above the thrust have been pushed up and over those below it. It is not uncommon for the relative movement between the rocks above and below a thrust to exceed several kilometres.

Tamarisk

Tamarix gallica

Folding in slate and pale grey siltstone beds, foreshore east of Marazion.

In more recent geological times, between five and 1.5 million years ago, sea levels were higher than at present. The platforms cut by wave-action of this period are still visible as the flat tops of the hills. The 130-metre platform is well displayed as a shelf around the Land's End Peninsula; the 90-metre platform accounts for the flat surface of the Lizard; and the flat topped hills around Carrick Roads are the remnants of a 70-metre platform. There are beds of sand and clay lying between 27 and 45 metres above present sea level around St Erth between Penzance and St Ives. These deposits were economically important in Victorian times when they were worked for moulding sand for use in the foundry at Hayle, and puddling clay, used as a waterproof lining for canals and dams.

Raven

Corvus corax

The low slate cliffs and sheltered coves and inlets of the scenically charming coastline of Carrick Roads and Falmouth Bay were formed less than one million years ago. Rivers and waves eroded rocks affected by fracture zones or geological faults within the otherwise resistant beds of sandstone and slate. Straight courses shown by some creeks and river valleys follow the line of these underlying geological faults which were caused by blocks of ground slipping against each other. The faults came about as sections of the earth's crust responded to stresses imposed by the slow but relentless forces of continental collision.

Ships laid up in the deep water of the drowned valley of the River Fal, south of Truro.

A view of Falmouth across the sheltered deep waters of Carrick Roads.

Carrick Roads has been used as a sheltered deep water anchorage at least since the time of Henry VIII and it has been protected by the gun forts of Falmouth and St Mawes castles. They have been used as recently as the second World War, indicating the strategic and economic value of the area over the centuries. Carrick Roads and its tributary creeks largely owe their present form and their depth of water to the action of very much larger rivers which flowed in these valleys during the ice ages of the last million years. Although the ice sheets which affected much of northern Europe barely reached Cornwall, the enormous volumes of water which were locked up within them during glacial cold periods caused the sea to fall to 150 metres below its present level. During these cold periods the rivers carved their valleys ever deeper as they ran across the low lying land exposed by the retreating sea. Carrick Roads and its tributaries are some of these valleys which were later drowned by the rising sea at the end of the ice ages about ten thousand years ago, creating a coast fretted by deep water inlets.

Green Woodpecker

Picus viridus

The valley of the River Cober between Helston and the sea at Loe Bar formed in a similar manner and encloses Loe Pool, the largest natural body of fresh water in Cornwall, now managed by the National Trust. Until the thirteenth century this valley allowed ships to sail up to the medieval port of Helston, one of the few sheltered ports on this stormy southern coast. The growth of the shingle bank of Loe Bar in the thirteenth century eventually blocked the valley to ships and dammed the stream allowing Loe Pool to develop. Legend has it that Jan Tregeagle (pronounced Tregail), a figure of Cornish folklore, was charged by the Devil to remove the sand from Berepper Beach. Unfortunately Jan dropped a sack which blocked the mouth of the River Cober.

Looking east across Loe Bar.

Before the rise in sea level, offshore areas were extensively forested. Traces of these now submerged forests, consisting of fallen logs and tree stumps about 4200 years old rooted in peat, are occasionally revealed during particularly low tides at Maenporth, near Falmouth, and between Long Rock and Chyandour near Penzance. Similar remnants of submerged forest of oak, hazel, birch and alder, together with remains of deer and human skulls were revealed during excavations at Market Strand in Falmouth in 1871 and in excavations for tin in Restronguet Creek. The legend of 'The Lost Land of Lyonesse' recounting stories of long abandoned villages beneath the sea between Land's End and the Isles of Scilly may have its origins in local folk history of the last four thousand years.

Although you may think of the Ice Age as being very much colder than today, there were a number of short periods in which the climate was a good deal warmer. Ice melting during these periods allowed sea levels to rise. Wave action along the higher coastlines

Rounded and highly polished pebbles which form Loe Bar. A high proportion is flint which has been derived from offshore.

A tree trunk projecting from the beach sand near Penzance representing part of a submerged forest.

cut flat platforms in the rocks up to eight metres above the present high tide level and deposited sand, shingle and boulders on them. Although these raised beaches are present around much of the coast, wave erosion is steadily removing them and exhuming the old cliffs which lie behind them. Particularly good examples of a raised beach are to be found in Sunny Cove, between Maenporth and Pennance Point, south west of Falmouth, between Cudden Point and St Michael's Mount in Mount's Bay and Pendower in Roseland.

Raised beach of sand and gravel resting on folded slate, Pendower.

At Godrevy Point, at the eastern end of St Ives Bay, the sand on the raised beach platform has been naturally cemented to make a highly porous, shelly sandstone, and can be seen as large blocks tumbled around the modern beach.

Raised beach of sand naturally cemented into sandrock, Godrevy.

The large areas of sand dunes, locally referred to as *towans*, have formed since the end of the last ice age by sand blown from the beaches by the prevailing westerly and southwesterly winter gales which affect the coasts of Cornwall. The dunes at Praa Sands rest upon peat dated as 1800 years old, which formed in a lagoon when the dunes blocked drainage into the sea. The sand has since encroached upon the peat as it advanced landwards. Although the main area of sand dunes in this part of Cornwall lie along the eastern side of St Ives' Bay, they can form on any westerly or southwesterly shore, such as those at Praa Sands and Jangye-ryn, which has a sandy beach but no high cliffs. Still to be seen in the towans between Hayle and Gwithian are the protective ramparts of sand which surrounded the buildings of a disused dynamite factory.

'Three miles of golden sand.' An oft quoted phrase used to describe the beaches and dunes between Hayle and Godrevy.

Yellow horned-poppy

Glaucium flavum

Bed of peat below sand dunes, Praa Sands.

As sea level rose at the end of the Ice Age it was accompanied by the infilling of the drowned valleys and creeks by silt brought down by rivers. In Restronguet Creek and in the River Hayle this silting up was dramatically accelerated by the deposition of fine-grained mineral tailings brought down by streams from the tin mining district in the centre of the peninsula. Up to 34 metres of alluvium is present in the River Hayle. In the Restronguet Creek, some places such as Devoran, were reported in 1698 as having a depth of water at low tide equivalent to 15 metres, but are now dry.

Silted up dock at Devoran; the stone wall on the right was used to support a lock gate.

Sea holly

Eryngium maritimum

Granite mooring post, Devoran Quay.

The rotting remains of silted up wharves at Devoran.

Cornish granite typically forms a landscape of gently rounded moorland. The skyline is broken only rarely by angular groups of rocks known as tors, slabs of rock seemingly piled one upon the other by some ancient pagan giant.

Granite tors on Trendrine Hill between Zennor and St Ives.

Much of the flatter ground of the Land's End or Penwith peninsula has been cleared and given over to pasture or cereal where soils are suitable. The wilder part of the peninsula has been given Environmentally Sensitive Area status. Farmers are rewarded for farming less intensively in order to conserve and enhance the landscape, wild life and features of historic importance. Exposed to salt-laden winds, trees are rare and usually stunted, preferring to grow more prolifically in the safety of sheltered valleys. Between St Just and St Ives the higher land is natural moorland where bracken, gorse and heather flourish on steeper more exposed slopes with thin acid soil. Carnmenellis and the high granite country to the south of Camborne and Redruth is farmed for the most part and has little moorland. The granite cliffs between Cape Cornwall and Mousehole give rise to some very fine coastal scenery. The sea has taken advantage of granite weakened by alteration along faults or workings on mineral lodes, forming steep sided chasms in the cliffs known locally as *zawns*. You may notice clusters of tiny walled fields, heavily overgrown and mostly disused, clinging to southerly facing slopes between Penberth Cove and Mousehole. These are the remains of a once thriving horticultural industry which produced early crops, especially daffodils and potatoes. Windbreaks of *escallonia, Fuchsia magellanica* along with *privet* were also employed and these species can still be seen growing in this area.

Spring squill

Scilla verna

Granite is generated as a result of continental plates colliding. In the case of Cornwall it was the same collision which squeezed the oceanic crustal rocks of the Lizard onto the land margin of a continent. Sedimentary rocks such as sandstone and mudstone make up a large proportion of the continental crust. When they are pushed down by the force of the collision, melting takes place giving rise to a liquid rock known as magma. A large, concealed body of granite, referred to as a *batholith*, forms a spine to Cornwall and generated smaller offshoots called *plutons*, such as Land's End and Carnmenellis, from a vast reservoir of molten rock about 280–290 million years ago.

Granite briefly explained
- *coarse crystalline igneous rock*
- *formed deep in the earth by melting of the lower crust*
- *rises slowly through the crust as a large molten globule, engulfing or shouldering aside other rock in its path*
- *crystals form as the melt cools slowly and solidifies*
- *now exposed by erosion which has removed the rocks above*

Individual crystals of the three most common minerals from which granite is made are usually readily identifiable.

Main granite minerals
- *quartz: grey and glassy*
- *feldspar: white tablets, but can be brown, pink or green*
- *mica: small flat glistening sheets, can be dark brown, pale brown, green or colourless*

Typical Cornish granite with large feldspar crystals.

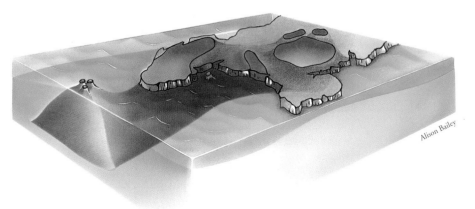

granite

other rocks

The granite batholith beneath west Cornwall and the Isles of Scilly.

Granite veins at Porthmeor Cove; the later thicker vein cutting and displacing the earlier thinner one.

Evidence of how the granite invaded the surrounding rocks is best seen at the contacts between granite and slate. Numerous veins of granite first penetrated these rocks before they were consumed by the rising pluton of granite magma. In some areas the granite failed to completely 'digest those rocks which it consumed', especially near the granite margin around Sennen Cove. Rounded, usually darker masses of different composition occur within the granite and are known to geologists as xenoliths, from the Greek meaning stranger stones. The Cornish miner referred to them as *furreners*. Granite veins are usually finer grained granite than the plutons because they cool more quickly and the mineral crystals have less time to grow. At **Porthmeor Cove**, west-south-west of Zennor, fine examples of granite veins can be seen cutting the slate and other veins near a small offshoot of the Land's End Granite.

Granite tors near the Basset Monument, Carn Brea.

Buzzard

Buteo buteo

Granite is a hard, strong rock when fresh but can be weakened by alteration and weathering. Exposures of the local granite plutons are uncommon with the exception of the magnificent cliffs of the Land's End area and a few isolated tors. Tors are blocky outcrops of upstanding resistant rock usually bearing the scars of erosion along joints, planes of weakness which formed within the rock as the granite cooled and contracted. Joints acted as channelways for alteration and when exposed to the elements they are selectively targeted by erosion. Horizontal joints are usually prominent in tors and can be seen at **Trendrine Hill**, between Zennor and St Ives, and at **Carn Brea** between Camborne and Redruth.

Weathering can give rise to smooth, bowl-like depressions in seemingly hard rock. Good examples of these, known locally as 'The Giant's Crocks and Kettles' or 'Cups and Saucers' may be seen on **Carn Brea**, just to the east of the monument. Until Victorian times these rock basins were thought to have been made by the Druids for use in their ceremonies. The sculpting is in fact caused by the repeated freezing of water in surface irregularities, the expanding ice gradually prising out individual mineral grains. The 27.5-metres high granite monument close by was dedicated in 1836 to the memory of Francis Basset, the first Lord de Dunstanville of Tehidy.

Weathered bowls on a granite slab, Carn Brea.

The Logan Rock, near Treen.

It is not uncommon for a block at the top of a tor or even a cliff to become detached from the bedrock because of weathering along joints. Blocks may weather into rounded shapes and it is sometimes possible to rock them to and fro with one hand. Such rocks are known by their Cornish name, *loganstones* (*log* = to heave or to move), and **Logan Rock** at Treen is a fine clifftop example. The rock weighs an estimated 65 tons and in 1824 Lieutenant Hugh Colvill Goldsmith of His Majesty's Navy, nephew of the poet, dislodged it with the help of his crew. Local pressure caused the Admiralty to threaten to withdraw his commission unless the rock was restored to its original position. Fortunately the rock had come to rest in a gully and not plunged into the sea. Although Goldsmith and his men from the revenue cutter *HMS Nimble*

Thrift

Armeria maritima

Fulmar

Fulmaris glacialis

did this most expertly, at a personal cost to himself of £130/8s/6d, the stone has never rocked as easily since. A public fund was started to help with the expense and it is believed that the Geological Society of London contributed £50. For some years after, the stone was kept chained and padlocked to prevent a repetition of this incident, but eventually, the absurdity of the situation was appreciated and the rock was set free.

Well-defined vertical jointing in granite, Lands End.

Land's End

In years gone by, the visitors to England's most westerly point parked their cars, gazed over the 'Lost Land of Lyonesse' to the Isles of Scilly and beyond towards America, before perhaps visiting the hotel to refresh themselves. All this has changed; except the view that is. The hotel is now part of a large 'theme park' setting out to inform the tourist of the area and bygone days. The complex also gives a home to numerous local craftsmen who can be seen at work, satisfying the endless demands for the mementoes we all take home to remind us of those blissful summer days.

The granite cliffs remain steadfast after interminable battles with mountainous seas whipped up by Atlantic gales. Although the cliffs are strong and stable, the adjoining paths and walkways had to be closed and extensive repairs carried out. The ceaseless tramp of feet over time wore away the grass allowing rainwater to strip off the thin soil cover and erode deep gullies in the subsoil.

In many of the granite outcrops it is possible to identify the constituent minerals: quartz, feldspar and dark mica. Feldspar commonly occurs in large, rectangular crystals known as megacrysts. The cliffs are known for their castle-like appearance caused by three sets of joints, two vertical and one horizontal. Just ten minutes of gentle walking to the south brings you to **Pordenack Point** where magnificent views of cliffs and majestic coastline are splendidly revealed.

Even at low tide it is highly dangerous to descend the cliffs to gain access to the shore. Should you wish to walk on the rock platform you may do so with great care on days of low spring tides from Sennen, to the north and Mill Bay (Nanjizal) to the south.

Enys Dodnan, Armed Knight and Longships: offshore granite rocks.

Looking from Pordenack Point towards Carn Boel with Gwennap Head in the distance.

Precariously perched blocks of granite, Pordenack Point.

Joint patterns in granite, Pordenack Point.

29

Cape Cornwall, St Just.

To the west of St Just lies **Cape Cornwall**, England's only cape. Although not made of granite, the spectacular views of granite cliffs to the south of this scenic promontory are most rewarding. The National Trust have care of this jewel in Cornwall's crown thanks to the far-sighted generosity of the Heinz Company who purchased it for the nation in 1987. **Porth Nanven** is the next cove to the south, reached by a narrow lane from St Just. The northern part of the cove is backed by a remarkable cliff of granite boulders. It is a remnant of a raised boulder beach which accumulated when the sea was at a higher level. The angular granite fragments above represent the weathered freeze-thaw debris that accumulated locally whilst glaciers were operating to the north during the Ice Age.

Boulders of granite forming a raised beach in a cliff at Porth Nanven near St Just.

At **Bosigran**, midway between St Just and St Ives, sheer cliffs of granite plunge into the ocean near Porthmoina Cove and have long been the haunt of rock climbers. Sherpa Tensing of Everest fame is known to have climbed here. Commando Ridge is a jagged comb of granite reaching down to the sea, named after the extensive military training which took place here during the period 1940-45.

Porthmoina Cove, separating Commando Ridge in the foreground from Bosigran Cliff.

Plymouth City Museums and Art Gallery collection

Plymouth porcelain figures made from Cookworthy's china clay.

Just how soft and weak granite can be is demonstrated where it is partly altered to china clay. Where hot water and gasses passed through fractures in the granite the feldspars are altered to clay. China clay was discovered in China in about the eighth century and called kaolin. William Cookworthy was a chemist and potter from Plymouth and in 1846 discovered the first source of this raw material in England on the slopes of **Tregonning Hill**, between Penzance and Helston. There are many small china clay workings in the Land's End Granite, most of which are flooded or overgrown, the most recently worked being **Bostraze**, east of St Just, which closed in the late 1980s.

At no great depth, the granite of south-west England tends to be hotter than the surrounding rocks. Heat is generated by a natural isotopic reaction constantly taking place within some of its minerals. Attempts have been made to recover this geothermal energy for commercial use by passing water through fractured hot rock at depth and pumping it back to the surface. Experiments were carried out at **Rosemanowas** granite quarry, just to the

Soft kaolinized granite, The fractures through which hot water passed now have become filled with quartz .

Foxglove

Digitalis purpurea

north of the Falmouth to Helston road at Longdowns where tall towers were recent, albeit temporary additions to the landscape.

Because of its strength and resistance to the elements, granite has been used locally as a building material for thousands of years. Neolithic and Bronze Age man, between 3500 and 400 years BC, built tombs, standing stones and stone circles in the Land's End Peninsula using blocks of weathered moorstone granite. **Lanyon Quoit**, a chamber tomb and **Men-an-tol**, a holed stone thought to have been the entrance to a tomb, can be found on the downs to the north-west of Madron. After collapsing during a storm in 1815, Lanyon Quoit was restored in 1824 under the supervision of Hugh Goldsmith after his success in replacing the Logan Rock to its original position. The capstone is not as high as it used to be, resting on three uprights instead of four and you are no longer able to ride a horse below as was previously the custom.

Men-an-tol near Madron. The stones were thought by many to have magical powers. Children were passed through the circular hole to cure them of rickets.

Lanyon Quoit near Madron.

Merry Maidens near Boleigh.

A pair of standing stones named the **Pipers**, at Boleigh, south-east of St Buryan, are both made of granite. Nearby are the **Merry Maidens**, a stone circle consisting of rectangular granite blocks. Local legend has it that the 'Maidens' were young girls turned into stone for dancing on the Sabbath and the two Pipers had been responsible for playing the music.

Stonechat

Saxicola torquata

In the Iron Age, which followed and persisted in Cornwall until long after the Roman invasion, hill forts such as **Castle-an-Dinas** and cliff castles like **Maen Castle** were common. **Chysauster**, to the north of Penzance, is a particularly fine example of a courtyard village with houses and streets. The forts and castles were mainly of earth and rock construction but the villages and field hedges were constructed of drystone walls utilising local stone, which in the Land's End Peninsula was invariably granite.

Chysauster, Iron Age Village.

33

Men Scryfa, *an inscribed standing stone.*

The Roman legacy in west Cornwall is restricted to a handful of milestones marking long-forgotten roads probably constructed for the purposes of trade. A *granite milestone* bearing the inscription *IMP CAES ANT GOR DIA NO PIO FEL* was dug up near Busveal in 1942, which translates as "To the Emperor, Caesar, Antonius Gordianus-Pious Fortunate." Gordian the third ruled from AD 238-244 suggesting that this is the earliest stone of its type to be found in Cornwall. A few quite large hoards of Roman coins have been found, mostly in the areas of tin streaming, which supports the likelihood of Roman trade links. After the Romans departed these shores much of their culture left with them. Archaeological evidence suggests that hill forts were re-occupied and the Cornish slipped back into their Iron Age ways, if indeed they ever gave them up. Early Christians followed the fashion of their Bronze Age forebears by erecting standing stones which date from the fifth and sixth centuries. They tended to be smaller and were inscribed to commemorate chiefs or well-known people. **Men Scryfa**, a granite pillar standing on the moorland at Bosullow, near Men-an-tol, bears the fading inscription which when translated means *Rialobranus, son of Cunovalus.* Wayside crosses, invariably made of granite, are probably Celtic-Christian in origin and made between the seventh and the eleventh centuries. Little is known about the use of granite as a building material until after the Normans had landed in the eleventh century. Many of the square-towered Cornish churches were constructed between the twelfth and fifteenth centuries.

Peregrine

Falco peregrinus

Towednack Parish Church dating from the thirteenth century and built of granite.

A fine example of the use of granite in a medieval building is **Carn Brea Castle**. This hunting lodge of the Basset family was built on a tor which can still be seen as part of the foundations.

Granite tor in the foundations of Carn Brea Castle.

Most of the granite used for building was moorstone, worked from loose blocks and surface exposures. As you walk over the open moorland you will come across rock outcrops which have a row of short, rounded channels along a face. A mason, recognizing the local joint pattern in the granite, would drill by hammer and chisel a series of short holes in a line along a joint with the knowledge that the rock will split cleanly in this direction. Into each hole two steel wedges known as *feathers* or *tares* are placed, with a third, known as a *plug*, between them. The plugs are struck in turn, gradually increasing the localized stresses until the rock splits. Evidence of this technique, known as 'plug and feathering', can also be observed on the numerous traditional gateposts of the area.

Plug and feather holes made by quarrymen to split granite blocks along joints.

Drilling holes by hand for setting explosives in hard rocks was a skillful and arduous task. On holidays, locally known as feast days, miners would compete to see who was the best driller and the blocks of granite which they used for the purpose can still be seen in Plen an Gwary, an old amphitheatre near the square in St Just.

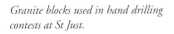

Granite blocks used in hand drilling contests at St Just.

35

Blackthorn

Prunus spinosa

Granite quarry used for testing rock drills, Carn Marth.

Hand drilling was superseded in about 1870 by drilling machines. In a quarry just north of the summit of **Carn Marth**, east of Redruth, you may observe the results of testing drilling equipment over the course of many years. The walls of the quarry bear a passing resemblance to gruyère cheese, amazingly peppered with small holes.

Cornish 'Cathedrals'

Truro

Ding Dong, Madron

It was not until the nineteenth century that granite was quarried in a big way. Stone from numerous quarries near **Penryn** was shipped out via Falmouth, and at Lamorna it was loaded directly into waiting boats and taken to London and all over the world. Many fine granite buildings exist locally, scattered liberally throughout the area. Mine engine houses were commonly constructed of granite. **Ding Dong**, north-west of Madron is a fine example and many others can be seen in the Camborne-Redruth and the St Just areas. The iron rails of the Redruth and Chacewater Railway, which carried coal to the mines in the nineteenth century, were mounted on rectangular granite blocks or sets. One of the last major constructions to use mainly granite was **Truro Cathedral,** completed in 1910.

Kittiwake

Rissa tridactyla

Minack Theatre, Porthcurno.

Although not strictly a building, the open-air auditorium of the **Minack Theatre**, just west of Porthcurno, does occupy a natural depression in the granite cliffs. It was largely the idea of Miss Rowena Cade who spent many hours of hard labour to turn the rough cliff-slope into a charming theatre which has continually evolved since its humble conception in 1930 and its first play, *The Tempest*, in 1932. The backdrop is a marvellous kaleidoscope of bustling fishing boats and ships which at dusk form a curtain of bobbing lights, guided from the wings by the beams of the Lizard and Wolf lighthouses.

Another fascinating open-air meeting place is **Gwennap Pit**, near the hamlet of Busveal to the east of Redruth. Said to be originally a collapsed mine working on the small granite pluton of Carn Marth, it was modified into a circular auditorium by miners and was a favourite preaching venue of John Wesley in the eighteenth century. Methodist services are still held here and a new visitor centre has been constructed.

Gwennap Pit.

5. Mining country

Engine House, Killifreth Mine.

As a visitor to Cornwall you will be sure to find the remnants of the mining industry a fascinating addition to the natural landscape. The ruined mine buildings are a solemn reminder of an industry which had its beginnings in the Bronze Age. Tin ore was first worked from gravels washed down from veins in rocks upstream. Copper ores could be collected from veins exposed in the cliffs and so the ingredients of bronze were readily available. Early examples of bronze ingots may be seen in the **Royal Cornwall Museum** in Truro. By Roman times, evidence of tin production, mainly from river gravels, is reasonably well established. Underground mining did not develop until the Middle Ages when it was limited to cliffs or valley sides where water could be drained by means of gravity through tunnels or adits. All these early sites were known collectively to later generations of Cornish miners as 'old men's workings'. The invention of gunpowder and advances in pumps increased the efficiency of mining. Steam pumps were developed by engineers such as Newcomen, Boulton and Watt, and Trevithick, which allowed mines to be worked to depths previously thought impossible. Dolcoath Mine, east of Camborne, was sunk to a depth of just over one kilometre and remains the deepest ever worked in Cornwall.

The area between Camborne and Redruth was one of the most heavily mined in the world.

Many minerals from Cornwall have pride of place in some of the finest mineral collections in the world. As well as tin and copper, the ores of arsenic, iron, lead, silver, tungsten and zinc have been worked in quantity. Rarer minerals include gold nuggets, found in the Carnon Valley, and the ores of bismuth, cobalt and nickel. In 1908, uranium ore was worked for its radium content from the dumps at Wheal Trenwith, St Ives. A few years later the mine was re-opened and a limited quantity was mined and supplied to Madame Curie in France for her research into radioactivity.

Mineralization briefly explained

- *heat from granite batholith*
- *water heated in fractures*
- *convection of hot water*
- *hot water extracts metallic salts from surrounding rock*
- *repeated circulation of fluid leads to concentration of salts*
- *deposition of metal ores from cooling water in fractures forming veins, locally known as lodes*

South Crofty Mine, Camborne.

Copper production in Cornwall declined in the 1850s and tin followed suit in the 1890s. This was due more to cheaper production in hitherto unexplored countries than the exhausting of Cornwall's reserves. Dredging alluvial tin in Malaya and digging copper ores from opencast pits in South America and Africa was so much easier and more profitable than working Cornwall's narrow, deep and unpredictable veins.

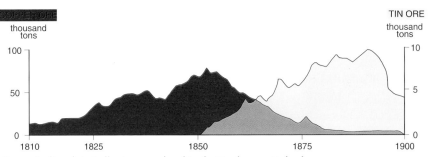

Copper (red) and tin (yellow) ores produced in the Cambourne–Redruth area 1810–1900, illustrating the decline of copper after 1857 and tin after 1895.

39

South Crofty Mine at Pool has weathered the storms of take-overs, amalgamations and temporary closure due to low tin prices to be Cornwall's only present working mine. The tall headframe at New Cooks Kitchen Shaft and the nearby ore silos dominate the skyline of the area.

New Cooks Kitchen Shaft and ore silos at South Crofty Mine.

Two mines which are used solely for training mining students are **Tywarnhayle** near Porthtowan and **King Edward** near Camborne.

To understand more about Cornish mining of days gone by, a visit to the museum on the site of the former **Geevor Tin Mine** at Pendeen is recommended. It is also possible to walk around the surface workings and examine the dressing floors where the tin ore was separated from the waste. You may even experience underground working conditions at **Poldark Mine**, Wendron, where guided tours of old workings are a feature of this heritage complex.

Engine House at Marriot's Shaft, South Wheal Frances, Basset Mines.

It is becoming increasingly difficult to find good mineral specimens on mine dumps. Much more rewarding and certainly a good deal safer is a visit to either the **Royal Cornwall Museum** at Truro or the **Camborne School of Mines' Museum** at Pool. On display are local specimens of the highest quality, many of which were collected whilst the mining industry was in full swing.

The gaunt remains of roofless engine houses are commonplace and have been widely adopted as a symbol of Cornish heritage. They were built on or near the outcrop of the mineral lodes, usually next to shafts. As the name suggests, they housed engines which were powered by steam. They were used for hauling ore and waste up the shaft, pumping water from underground and crushing ore at surface. It is usual for most mine buildings to be constructed of local rough stone with worked cornerstones and brickwork around the window openings. A chimney is commonly located at a corner at the opposite end to the sturdier wall upon which the beam of the engine was balanced. The chimney is also made from rough stone and has a marked taper. The narrow diameter of the topmost third of the height of the stack commonly required it to be built of brick.

Engine House at Pascoe's Shaft, South Wheal Frances, Basset Mines.

The engine houses on the **Crowns** section of **Botallack Mine**, situated between a steep cliff and a treacherous reef, testify to man's ingenuity in his pursuit of mineral wealth. The lower of the two engines was built first and used to pump water in Crowns Shaft from workings which extended for about threequarters of a kilometre under the sea.

Engine Houses, Crowns Section, Botallack Mine.

To save space on this restricted site the chimney was unusually constructed on the inside of the house. The higher of the two engines was later used to haul men and ore in the Boscawen Diagonal Shaft which inclined beneath the waves.

*Man-engine
at Dolcoath.*

About a kilometre to the north-east lies the **Levant Mine**. Famous for producing vast tonnages of copper, over 5000 tons per year at its peak from rich lodes under the sea, it is infamous for the man-engine disaster of 1919 when 31 miners lost their lives. The man-engine was a primitive device for conveying miners up and down a shaft. It consisted of baulks of timber fastened together to form a segmented wooden pillar which was suspended from a beam operated by the engine at the top of the shaft, slowly moving up and down under its power. Platforms fixed to the pillar moved up and down through a height of three and a half metres allowing a miner to step off onto platforms fixed to the side of the shaft. By repeatedly riding the engine and stepping off, the miner travelled up or down the shaft, a journey which took twenty five minutes. On the fatal afternoon of October 20th, the linkage joining the timber pillar to the mechanism of the steam engine broke, causing a catastrophic collapse, cascading bodies and debris into the pitch darkness below. The deeper levels were never worked again and the mine closed in 1929.

The workings of Levant extend more than one and a half kilometres out to sea and in the upper levels on a stormy day it was possible to hear the thunderous clunk of the restless boulders on the sea floor.

Nearby at **Skip Shaft**, used until recently by Geevor Mine, an engine house has been renovated complete with the 30-inch

Engine House at Skip Shaft, Levant Mine, containing a preserved winding engine.

whim or winding engine. This engine, with a cylinder diameter of thirty inches, is relatively small in comparison to many pumping engines which required greater power. The engine has been restored to working order and it is maintained by the National Trust who steam it up at intervals during the summer months. Other mine buildings tended to be more flimsy than the engine houses and have not survived the ravages of time. An exception to this is a fine group at the **South Wheal Frances** section of **Bassett Mines** near Piece, east of Camborne.

A comprehensive group of mine buildings at South Wheal Frances, Basset Mines

An interesting structure known as a calciner, was used for roasting ores of arsenic and can be seen at **Botallack Mine**, to the north of St Just. The ruins of the square building can still be seen where the ore was heated on firebricks on a revolving iron table. A collapsed flue leads to a double bank of snaking tunnels inter-connected by a bridge and called a labyrinth. Here the arsenical fumes cooled, depositing arsenic oxide whilst a final flue carried the residual smoke and fumes to a 30 metre high chimney, a total distance of nearly 250 metres. The product was periodically shovelled out and bagged up for sale, mainly to America where it was used in the cottonfields to discourage the attentions of the boll weevil.

An artists cut-away diagram of the arsenic calciner and labyrinth, Botallack Mine. Red arrows show former course of fumes.

Richard Bell

Gorse

Ulex europaeus

Iron ochre in water flowing from the County Adit, Mount Wellington.

The mining landscape of today has evolved through numerous decades of industrial devastation. Tumbledown buildings, untidy piles of rock and the scars of long-disused excavations combine together to make scenes of depressing dereliction. In many cases the dumps and surrounding areas contain sufficient toxic residues to prevent the growth of vegetation. Twentieth century structures of rust-stained concrete used to crush and dress ore do nothing to enhance the appearance of a despoiled countryside robbed of its natural charm. However, nature is making a supreme effort to redress the balance by reclaiming what was once lost, with ivy, gorse and heather retaking spoils previously won by pick and *gad,* a Cornish chisel

Rivers and streams ran red or brown with ochreous iron from mineral dressing, and the Red River lived up to its name. The colourful contents and tin ore polluted the sea and beaches at **Gwithian**. Downstream from the mineral dressing floors the river banks were littered with a succession of small works, each attempting to remove the last ounce of tin ore from the ruddy waters. The fine suspension of ore and other minerals was washed through a series of pits, the heavier grains settling to the bottom.

Some of the sand in the coastal dunes was brought down by rivers from the tin mining areas and contains a small proportion of tin. At **Gwithian** in St Ives Bay, the dunes were worked when economic conditions permitted and the remains of the separation plant are still visible near the mouth of the Red River.

Considerable amounts of tin, together with a little gold, have been washed down from the mineralized area during the last million years. Because tin ore is relatively heavy, much of it was deposited in the beds of the rivers as tin-rich gravel covered by deposits of silt and clay. Tin-rich alluvial gravel has been worked repeatedly, for example at Marazion and the Hayle River. In Restronguet Creek the extraction of tin was particularly bizarre. Before 1800 the tin-bearing gravel was won by digging pits within the creek, protected from the tidal water by an enclosing dam. Although parts of this dam are still visible as a low mound within the creek, the dam was breached in 1800 and the workings flooded. Between 1822 and 1873 the gravel was worked by underground mining within the soft, alluvial sands and clays.

Recent dereliction at Wheal Jane.

In recent years it is most fortunate that the importance of our industrial heritage has been recognised and some significant sites have been conserved. Decaying engine houses have been restored and as well as Levant, the National Trust cares for two steam engines at **East Pool Mine**, between Camborne and Redruth. The 30-inch winding engine at Mitchell's Shaft lies just to the south of the main road and is operated by electric motor for parties of visitors. The 90-inch pumping engine at Taylor's Shaft lies some way to the north with the initials 'EPAL' of East Pool and Agar

Cylinder head and piston rod of pumping engine, Robinson's Shaft, South Crofty.

Limited on the tall chimney stack. A third engine nearby, also in the care of the Trust is the 80-inch pumping engine at Robinson's Shaft, **South Crofty**, but being a working mine access is not readily available to visitors.

A considerable area of open country to the south of Camborne and Redruth, laid waste by mining, has been examined as a result of a scheme partly sponsored by local government, the **Mineral Tramways Project**. An inventory of industrial archaeological sites has been drawn up and conservation and amenity objectives identified. Work has commenced to conserve engine houses, to create a network of trails along former mineral tramways and railways, and generally tidy up much of the neglected countryside.

Winding engine at Mitchell's Shaft, East Pool Mine.

Efforts to clean up the rivers, coupled with a decline in mineral dressing has met with great success. The Red River flows clear, no longer colouring the surf at Gwithian a lurid shade of pink.

At the height of the mining industry's boom in the first half of the nineteenth century, many small ports were working to service the demand for coal, timber and other mining supplies, and to ship out copper ore to the smelters in South Wales. **Portreath** is one such port with its granite-built harbour still intact. It was first linked to the mining area by the Poldice Tramway,

Red sea at Pendeen in the days when tin ore was washed at Geevor Mine.

begun in 1809. This horse-drawn plateway gave the mines of the Scorrier and St Day districts a route to the sea and was Cornwall's first railway. In 1837 Portreath was joined via an inclined plane, to the Hayle Railway which gave the Camborne area a double access to the sea and a link with the foundry and smelter at Hayle.

The Redruth and Chacewater Railway was opened in 1826 which provided the mines of Redruth, Lanner and Gwennap with an access to the newly constructed harbour at **Devoran**. It was horsedrawn before converting to steam in 1854. An interested visitor, exploring the peaceful streets of Devoran, can still find relics of granite tramways used to transport ore to the quayside as well as silted up remains of former quays amongst bungalow gardens.

Mineral tramway now in a Devoran garden.

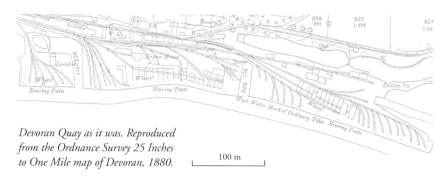

Devoran Quay as it was. Reproduced from the Ordnance Survey 25 Inches to One Mile map of Devoran, 1880.

100 m

Tin was also smelted locally at **Point** until the early part of this century, but the only evidence that you will find are pieces of black glassy slag on the foreshore. Although this quiet backwater retains few clues to its busy industrial past, we were reminded of its earlier associations with the mining industry when in 1992 the ochreous water from the Wheal Jane Mine contaminated the waters of Restronguet Creek and Carrick Roads.

Hayle's industrial heritage is similar but easier to appreciate because it was more recently active. The ruins of the foundry are still visible, though crumbling fast. Evidence of its tin and copper smelters is limited to the curious black blocks used to build the quays, embankments and a bridge in the now silted-up harbour at Copperhouse and various local buildings. These were made by pouring the molten slag from the tin smelter into metal moulds - an early effort at recycling.

Engine house preservation in progress at East Wheal Grenville.

46

Bridge built of slag blocks, Copperhouse.

Flow structure in slag block, evidence of its molten history.

Although the mining industry has almost departed from the area, the dwellings of the miners still survive. Their cottages were mainly built from the cheapest materials available, either boulders cleared from fields or mine waste. In a rural setting, the terraces of **Lower Boscaswell and Carnyorth** are notably attractive; many are now used as holiday homes. In Camborne and Redruth similar terraces may be more substantial but the surroundings are much less convivial. In marked contrast are the detached and well-built houses of the planned industrial village of **Halsetown**, south of St Ives, named after James Halse MP., solicitor and mining venturer. He built it in the 1830s to secure the franchise of his workers under the 1832 Reform Act and retain his seat of St Ives Borough.

Slag blocks in chequer-board pattern in farm buildings at Phillack.

The mining industry was supported by iron foundries which specialized in making mining equipment. Ships from Scandinavia sailed up Restronguet Creek to unload coal for the **Perran Foundry** and timber for mine props at Perran Wharf, now the site of the Norway Inn. The beam engines made by **Harvey's of Hayle** were not only supplied to many mines in Cornwall but were used to pump water in many parts of the country and around the world. The ironwork for Brunel's Tamar Bridge was also made by Harvey's. Today, with local mining almost gone, CompAir Holman bravely soldier on in the Camborne area making compressors and other mining equipment, the survivors of an industry devoted to the support of local mining

Former miners cottages, Boscaswell.

Cast-iron door lintel, Perran Foundry.

6. Where to go and what to see

LIZARD PENINSULA

1	Gabbro 'crusairs', Crousa Downs	5	Serpentine, Kynance Cove
2	Basalt dykes in gabbro, Coverack	6	Soapstone, Gew-graze
3	Collapsed sea cave, Cadgwith	7	Pillow lava, Mullion Island
4	Schist, Lizard Point		

LOW ROLLING COUNTRY

1	Raised beach, Sunny Cove	7	Raised beach, Cudden Point to Marazion
2	Submerged forest, Maenporth	8	Fragmented lava, Great Hogus
3	Shingle bar, Loe Bar	9	Submerged forest, Long Rock to Chyandour
4	Volcanic sills, Porthleven	10	Volcanic rock, Penlee Quarry
5	Sand dunes on peat, Praa Sands	11	Pillow lava, Burthallan Cliff
6	Volcanic rock headland, Cudden Point	12	Raised beach, Godrevy

LANDS END PENINSULA AND CARNMELLIS UPLANDS

1	Granite cliffs, Pordenack Point		**Historic Granite Structures**	
2	Granite cliffs, Land's End	16	Chamber tomb, Lanyon Quoit	Neolithic & Bronze Age
3	Xenoliths in granite, Sennen	17	Holed stone, Men-an-tol	
4	Boulders in raised beach, Porth Nanven	18	Standing stones, The Pipers	
5	Granite cliffs, Cape Cornwall	19	Stone circle, Merry Maidens	
6	Drill holes in granite, Plen an Gwary, St Just	20	Hill fort, Castle-an-Dinas	Iron Age
7	Altered granite (china clay), Bostraze	21	Cliff castle, Mayon Castle	
8	Granite cliffs, Bosigran	22	Courtyard village, Chysauster	
9	Granite veins, Porthmeor Cove	23	Granite milestone, Gwennap Roman	
10	Granite tors, Trendrine Hill	24	Inscribed stone, Bosullow Early Christian	
11	Logan stone, Logan Rock, Treen	25	Granite-built engine house,	Medieval & Recent
12	Altered granite (china clay), Tregonning Hill		Ding Dong Mine	
13	Granite tors, Carn Brea	26	Cathedral, Truro	
14	Quarry for test drilling, Carnmarth	27	Amphitheatre, Gwennap Pit, Busveal	
15	Geothermal energy site, Rosemanowas Quarry	28	Open air Theatre, Minack	

MINING COUNTRY

1	Minerals, Royal Cornwall Museum, Truro	14	Sand dunes worked for tin, Gwithian
2	Tin-rich gravel workings, Point	15	Harvey's Foundry, Hayle
3	Evidence of tin smelter, Point	16	Black Bridge of slag blocks, Copperhouse
4	Historic quays and tramways, Devoran	17	Minerals, Royal Geological Society, Penzance
5	Perran Foundry, Perranarworthal	18	Planned industrial village, Halsetown
6	Training mine, Tywarnhayle	19	Local Cornish life, Zennor Wayside Museum
7	Mine buildings, South Wheal Frances	20	Old mining village, Lower Boscaswell
8	Pumping engine, East Pool Mine	21	Mining, Geevor Tin Mine Museum
9	Winding engine, East Pool Mine	22	Old mining village, Carnyorth
10	Pumping engine, South Crofty Mine	23	Winding engine, Skip Shaft, Levant Mine
11	Minerals, Camborne School of Mines Museum	24	Arsenic calciner, Botallack Mine
12	Training mine, King Edward Mine	25	Engine houses, Crowns section, Botallack Mine
13	Poldark Tin Mine and Museum, Wendron		